Decodable Reader Library

Unit 2 Outside My Door

Contents

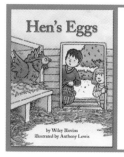

Fox on a Rock

by Marsha Gilmore
illustrated by Aleksey Ivanov

Mom Fox is very sad.
Where is Bob Fox now?

Is Bob Fox in Frog's pond?
Bob is not in Frog's pond.

Is Bob Fox in Tom's box?
Bob is not in Tom's box.

Mom Fox is sad.
Mom sits on a rock.
Mom can use help.

Ant can help Mom Fox.
Now Mom can see Bob Fox!

Hen's Eggs

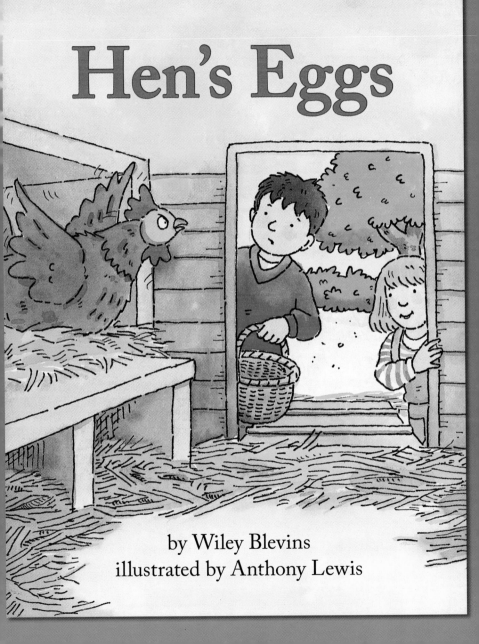

by Wiley Blevins
illustrated by Anthony Lewis

"Ben, can Mom fix eggs?"

"Yes, Meg. Get two eggs."

"We have one egg.
Get Hen's egg, Ben.
Get her egg."

Does Hen have eggs?
Ben is in Hen's pen.
Hen is mad!

Meg yells for Mom
and Dad.
They will help.

Mom will not fix eggs.
Mom will fix ham!

This Fish, That Fish

by Maryann Dobeck

This is a fish tank.
It has lots of fish.
Can you see them?

14

Fish can eat a lot.
Who can help them?
This man gets food.

Some fish are thin.
This fish is fat!

This fish is fat, too.
This fish can puff up!

Is that a fish?
No, it is a crab.
It has a thin shell.

The men are on a ship.
They fish with big nets.

This shop sells fresh fish.
Get some fish to eat!

Just for Fun!

by Anna Keyes

Where do Ed and Liz live?
They run and play here.
This band is a lot of fun!

It is hot in the sun.
Kids jump in and
get wet.

Kids can hit and run.
Gus hit it up, up, up.
It went into a mitt.

Kids jump up and
jump out.
It is fun, fun, fun!

Kris sees many ducks.
He drops bits of crust.
It is just for fun!

Come On, Clem!

by Lucy Floyd
illustrated by Mick Reid

"Let's plan a show!"
yells the Math Club.
"Come on, Clem!"

Clem tells them NO.
Ann tells Clem,
"You can dress up!"

"OK, then," Clem nods.
"I want three desks."

Clem cuts a flat blob.
Did Clem make a sled?
Can Clem put it on?

Clem is under it!
"It's a bug," he yells.
"It has six legs!"

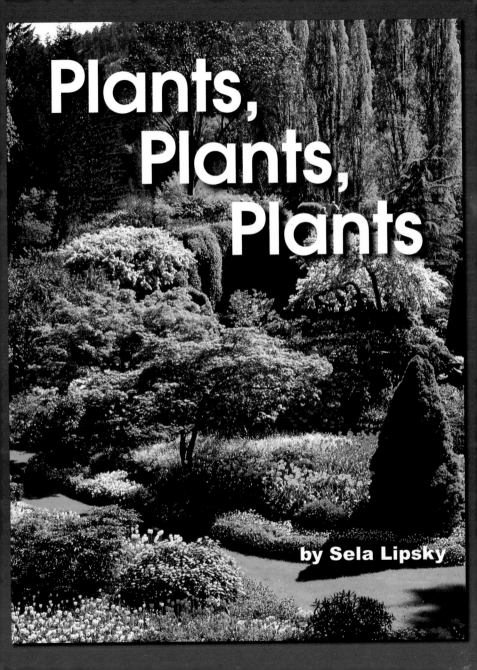

Plants, Plants, Plants

by Sela Lipsky

A plant can be little.
A plant can get big.

This plant is big.
Do not tap it!
This plant can prick.

You can pluck this plant.
This plant can mend you.

Did the sun get you hot?
Do you have a red rash?
Rub the plant on the rash.

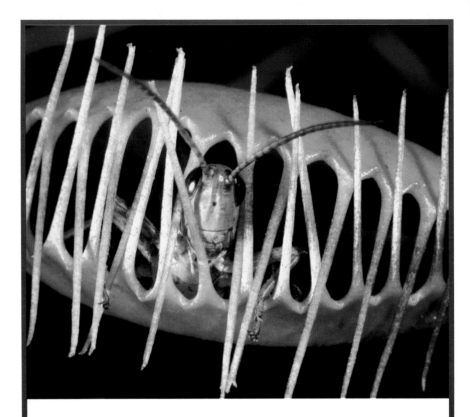

This odd plant can shut
bugs up in its trap.
Then it can crush them!

Bugs will pick this plant.
But you will not pick it.
Quick, run away!

It's not too late to shop.
You can get many plants.
Set them in the sun.

Unit 2: Outside My Door

Fox on a Rock
page 1

to use with *Animal Moms and Dads*
WORD COUNT: 58

DECODABLE WORDS
Target Phonics Element
short /o/o
Bob, box, Fox, Frog's, Mom, not, on, pond, rock, Tom's
Words Using Previously Taught Skills
Ant, can, in, is, sad, sits

HIGH-FREQUENCY WORDS
help, now, use, very
Review: a, see, where

Hen's Eggs
page 7

to use with *Little Red Hen*
WORD COUNT: 51

DECODABLE WORDS
Target Phonics Element
short /e/e
Ben, egg, eggs, get, Hen, Hen's, let, Meg, pen, yells, yes
Words Using Previously Taught Skills
and, can, Dad, fix, ham, in, is, mad, Mom, not, will

HIGH-FREQUENCY WORDS
does, her, one, they, two
Review: for, have, help, we

This Fish, That Fish

to use with *A Prairie Dog Home* **WORD COUNT: 84**

DECODABLE WORDS
Target Phonics Elements
digraphs /sh/*sh*, /th/*th*
that, them, thin, this, with
shell, ship, shop, fish, fresh
Words Using Previously Taught Skills
a, big, can, crab, fat, get, gets, has, is, it, lot, lots, man, men, nets, on, puff, sells, tank, up

HIGH-FREQUENCY WORDS
eat, no, of, some, who
Review: are, do, help, see, the, they, to, too, you

CONCEPT WORD
food

Just for Fun!

page 21

to use with *The Fun Kids' Band* **WORD COUNT: 74**

DECODABLE WORDS
Target Phonics Element
short /u/*u*
crust, ducks, fun, Gus, jump, just, sun, up, run
Words Using Previously Taught Skills
a, and, band, bits, can, drops, Ed, get, hit, hot, in, is, it, kids, Kris, Liz, lots, mitt, run, this, went, wet

HIGH-FREQUENCY WORDS
into, live, many, out
Review: for, go, he, here, of, play, see(s), the, they, where

for use with *On My Way to School* **WORD COUNT: 61**

DECODABLE WORDS

Target Phonics Elements

l blend /bl/ *bl-*
blob

l blend /kl/ *cl-*
Clem, club

l blend /fl/ *fl-*
flat

l blend /pl/ *pl-*
plan

l blend /sl/ *sl-*
sled

Words Using Previously Taught Skills

a, Ann, bug, can, cuts, desks, did, dress, has, I, is, it, it's, legs, let's, math, nods, OK, on, six, tells, them, then, up, yells

HIGH-FREQUENCY WORDS

make, put, show, three, under, want

Review: come, he, no, the, you

Review **WORD COUNT: 95**

DECODABLE WORDS
Review Target Phonics Elements
short /o/o
  hot, not, odd, on, shop
short /e/e
  get, mend, red, set, them, then
digraph /sh/sh
  crush, rash, shop, shut
digraph /th/th
  them, then, this
short /u/u
  bugs, but, pluck, rub, run, shut, sun, up
l blends
  plants, pluck

Words Using Previously Taught Skills
a, at, big, bugs, but, can, did, has, in, is, it, its, it's, pat, pick, plant, plants, prick, quick, tap, trap, will

HIGH-FREQUENCY WORDS
Review: away, be, do, have, late, little, many, the, to, too, you